The Little Golden Book of JOKES & RIDDLES

Compiled by E. D. EBSUN
Illustrated by JOHN O'BRIEN

A GOLDEN BOOK, NEW YORK
Western Publishing Company, Inc., Racine, Wisconsin 53404

 Library of Congress Catalog Card Number: 82-83069 ISBN 0-307-02115-7 / ISBN 0-307-60192-7 (lib. bdg.)
C D E F G H I J

Knock, knock.
Who's there?

Lettuce.
Lettuce who?
Lettuce out, it's cold in here.

Knock, knock.
Who's there?

Freeze.
Freeze who?
Freeze a jolly good fellow!

What has one horn and gives milk?

A milk truck.

MR. SLOAN: Does that cow give milk?

FARMER McCOY: No, sir. We have to take it from her.

WAITER: How did you find your steak, sir?

MR. DURWOOD: I looked under a mushroom and there it was.

MR. DE WITT: Waiter, what is this fly doing in my soup?

WAITER: The backstroke.

MRS. WRIGHT: I would like a pair of alligator shoes.

CLERK: Certainly, madam. What size
does your alligator wear?

MRS. WRIGHT: Can I put this wallpaper on myself?

CLERK: Yes, ma'am, but it looks
a lot better on the wall.

How do you keep a skunk from smelling?

Hold its nose.

How do you keep an elephant from charging?

Take away its credit card.

MRS. WRIGHT: Timmy, did you take a bath today?

TIMMY: Why, is one missing?

JULIO: I can't walk any farther.
My shoes hurt too much.

CAROLYN: Why, that's because you
have them on the wrong feet.

JULIO: But these are the only
feet I have!

MRS. MARTIN: Dawn, did you make
your bed today?

DAWN: Yes, Mom. But I think it would
have been easier to buy one.

She was expecting some change in the weather.

TIMMY: Where are you going?

LAMONT: To the grocery store.

TIMMY: Are you going to take a bus?

LAMONT: I don't think so. My mother would just make me give it back.

DAWN: I was on the TV today.

KELLY: You're kidding! How long were you on?

DAWN: Not long. When my mother saw me sitting there, she made me get off.

MIKE: I've been skating since I was two years old.

LAMONT: Wow! You must be tired!

JENNIFER: Why is your dog spinning around and around like that?

DAWN: He's a watchdog. He's winding himself up.

What has four wings and flies?

Two canaries.

What has four wheels and flies?

A garbage truck.

Why do birds fly south in winter?

Because it's too far to walk.

What is gray, has four legs, big ears, a tail, and a trunk?

A mouse going on vacation.

MRS. DE WITT: Won't you join me in a cup of tea?

MRS. DURWOOD: Do you think there's enough room for both of us?

MRS. SLOAN: My daughter's gone on a cruise.

MRS. MARTIN: Jamaica?

MRS. SLOAN: No, she wanted to go.

FARMER MCCOY: How did you come to fall in the pond?

MR. SLOAN: I didn't come to fall in the pond. I came to fish.

What's the best way to catch a fish?

Have someone throw it to you.

What ten-letter word starts with g-a-s?

A-u-t-o-m-o-b-i-l-e.

What has one foot on each side
and one in the middle?

A yardstick.

KELLY: My mother knitted three socks for my brother in the army.

MIKE: Why three socks?

KELLY: He wrote and said he had grown another foot.

What do you get if you put a mother duck
and five ducklings into a box?

A box of quackers.

What's the difference between
a fish and a piano?

You can't tuna fish.

What kind of ears do engines have?

Engineers.

Why did the elephant sit on the marshmallow?

To keep from falling in the cocoa.

What time is it when an elephant sits on a fence?

Time to mend the fence.

Why did the cow
go over the mountain?

Because she couldn't go under the mountain.

How do you get down off an elephant?

You don't get down off an elephant.
You get down off a duck.

Why does the giraffe have such a long neck?

Because its head is so far from its body.

MRS. DURWOOD: Why don't you take Kelly to the zoo?

MR. DURWOOD: Certainly not. If the zoo wants her, let them come and get her.

JENNIFER: Did you know it takes three sheep to make a sweater?
DAWN: I didn't even know sheep could knit!
Where do sheep go to get their hair cut?
The baa-baa shop.

TEACHER: Give me a sentence with the word "gruesome" in it.

JULIO: The man stopped shaving and gruesome whiskers.

TEACHER: Give me a sentence using the word "fascinate."

CAROLYN: My blouse has nine buttons, but I can only fascinate.

What is the last thing you take off before going to sleep?

Your feet off the floor.